The XYZ Book

by Lynn Maslen Kertell
pictures by Sue Hendra and John R. Maslen

Scholastic Inc.

New York • Toronto • London • Auckland • Sydney • Mexico City • New Delhi • Hong Kong • Buenos Aires

X-ray of fox

Yawning yak   Zany zebra

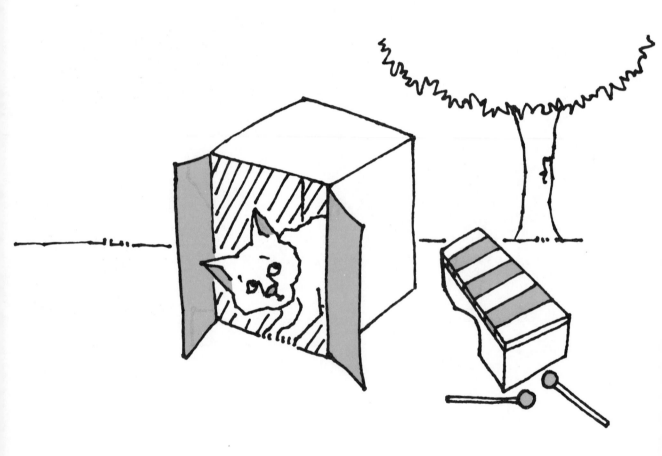

A fox in a box

hides from a T. rex.

Yellow jackets

spin yak yarn.

Zebras in zoot suits

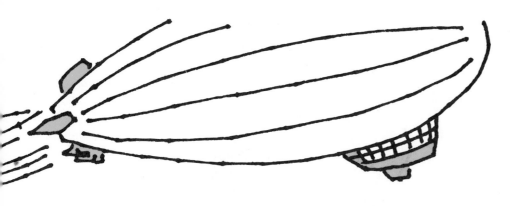

wave to a zooming zeppelin.

Fox uses yak yarn to make a

zany zoot suit for T. rex.

Look for these **x, y,** and **z** words in this book.

yak	zany
yarn	zebra(s)
yawning	zeppelin
yellow jackets	zooming
	zoot suit(s)

Few words start with the letter x, but many end with it. Look for: box, fox, and T. rex.

Look for these additional **x, y,** and **z** words in the pictures: xylophone, yo-yo, zinnias, and zipper.